THE PARABLE OF THE

Workers in the Vineyard

Matthew 19:30–20:16
for children

Written by Jonathan Schkade
Illustrated by Ed Koehler

CONCORDIA PUBLISHING HOUSE • SAINT LOUIS

"The last will be first,
And the first will be last."
Heaven's not just for
The strong and the fast.

"So then," said Jesus,
"I will tell you about
A master whose kindness
Was great beyond doubt.

"This master went out
To select men to toil
And tend to his vineyard,
His grapes, and his soil.

"The men there said, 'Fine.
But we want our full due,
A denarius each,
To work now for you.'

"The master agreed
And sent them to their job,
But later in town
He saw a small mob.

"A sad group of men
Was just sitting around,
So the master said,
'Come. You'll all work my ground.'

"After three full hours,
He went hiring again.
Then another three passed,
And still he found men.

"Though day was half gone,
He promised each guy,
'I'll pay you what's fair
For the work you supply.'

"Of course they signed on
For a job of this sort—
Their families were hungry,
And work time was short.

"Amazingly, then,
Near the day's very end,
The master found more
To his vineyard to send.

"After only one hour
Came the close of the day.
The last were called first
To pick up their pay.

"The one-hour men
Received a surprise—
An entire day's wage
Awaited these guys.

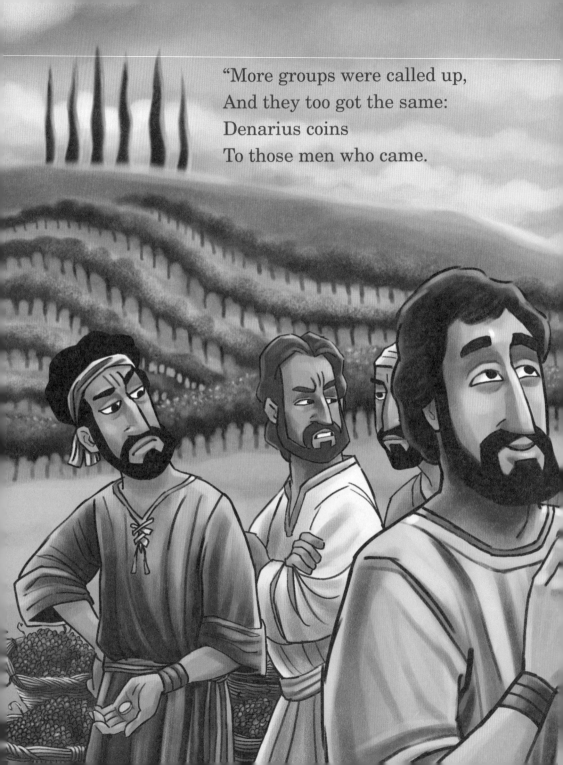

"More groups were called up,
And they too got the same:
Denarius coins
To those men who came.

"At last trudged the men
Who had worked the whole time
And expected a bonus
Of more than a dime.

"Instead, from the master
Each simply received
A denarius coin,
Just as they'd agreed.

"At once these men whined,
'This is really unfair.
You paid them like us,
Who have sweat in our hair!

" 'We've labored much longer,
Through the heat of the day!'
'But,' said the master,
'You agreed to this pay.

" 'Besides,' he went on,
'What cash did you lose?
Can't I give my money
Away as I choose?'

"Know the last will be first.
And the first will be last,"
And each will receive
Rewards that are vast.

Both those who've worked years
To spread God's good Word
And those who at death
Claim Christ as their Lord

Will get from their God
What Jesus has won:
A heavenly home
With Father and Son.

Dear Parent,

If read as a simple story about working and paychecks, it doesn't seem fair at all that someone who works hard all day is paid the same amount as someone who works only part of the day. Equal pay has long been a point of discussion in our world. But Jesus' parables are not simple stories.

Like the vineyard owner in search of workers, Jesus seeks us out and invites us to serve Him. We respond to His call, receive His good gifts, and acknowledge that eternal life in heaven is the wage we want. Some of God's faithful labor long and hard in this world. Some serve for only a short time or come to faith late in life. But in the end, all those who believe in Jesus as Lord and Savior will receive the same compensation. The Master gives us all the same wage regardless of our effort or the timing of it.

What truly isn't fair is that God gives us something better than what we've earned—He gives us heaven. Jesus tells us this story to show that He has a purpose for us in this life and that He gives us the promise of salvation and heaven freely. We have not earned that. We are saved by His grace.

When you read this story with your child, you might explain it by saying that there are many times when things seem to be unfair, and on this earth, it's true that there is much that is not fair. But Jesus loves all of us the same, He wants us all to believe in and love Him, and He offers all of us the promise of forgiveness and salvation.

The Editor